Key Spelling

Contents

unit 1

High-frequency words and syllabic patterns

 Key idea

Long words are easier to spell if you divide them up into syllables, like this:

unpainted has three syllables = un/paint/ed
colourfully has four syllables = col/our/ful/ly

You will see that many of these syllables are prefixes and suffixes. Once you have learned to spell these, you will know how to spell the parts of many words.

Try it out! •

Draw a grid in your book like the one below. Then sort the words into four lists: words with two syllables, words with three syllables, words with four syllables and words with five syllables.
(0.25 mark for each word you put in the correct list)

two syllables	three syllables	four syllables	five syllables
ladder	camera	directory	contradictory

meanwhile	glossary	spherical	plural	singular
climate	soldier	biography	literacy	rhythm
adjective	division	Victorian	triangular	multiplication
punctuate	addition	synonym	calculation	photography
circle	dialogue	decoration	syllable	biographical
industrial	pollution	exploration	cylinder	preposition
quality	question	consonant	finally	subtraction
period	whispered	rectangle	grammatical	composition

Keep practising!

One syllable is missing from one word in each sentence. Add the correct syllable so that the word fits in the sentence. Write the word in your book.

(1 mark for each correct answer)

1 I made an observa_____ every hour.
2 We collected lots of evid_____.
3 My predic_____ turned out to be right.
4 My first measure_____ was not accurate enough.
5 Copper wire is a good conduct_____ of electricity.
6 We wanted to investig_____ what helped the plant grow.
7 We covered the tank with transpar_____ plastic.
8 We chose cardboard because it is flexib_____.
9 We wanted to know which materi_____ dried quickest.
10 We connected the wire to a batter_____.

Take up the challenge!

Which syllable is missing from all the words in each list? Write out the words, adding the missing syllable.

(2 marks for each correct answer)

1 decor_____tion   alliter_____tion   appar_____tus   gener_____tion
2 environ_____   measure_____   equip_____   experi_____
3 subtrac_____   fric_____   instruc_____   addi_____
4 syllab_____   triang_____   rectang_____   ridd_____
5 natur_____   plur_____   cylindric_____   electric_____

3

unit 2 Words with double consonants

 Key idea

Short vowel sounds in the first syllable of words with two syllables are usually followed by a doubled consonant:

ladder   balloon   rubbish   rattle

This pattern is easy to see in a pair of words like **hoping** and **hopping**.

These consonants are never doubled:

h   j   k   q   v   w   x

Try it out! ••

Complete these words by adding a single or double consonant.
(0.5 mark for each correct answer)

ra__it   mi__le   ea__y   di__erent   gi__le

fa__ous   umbre__a   da__le   noi__y   li__le

wo__le   gi__y   to__ee   rea__on   ye__ow

o__osite   tomo__ow   po__ible   re__ind   bu__on

Choose the word that fits in the sentence. Then write the sentence again. *(1 mark for each correct answer)*

1 striped/stripped   He was wearing a _____ tie.
2 bonny/bony   He pointed at me with a _____ finger.
3 dinner/diner   I'll see you after _____.
4 comma/coma   I left a _____ out of the sentence.
5 planing/planning   I was _____ my story.
6 scarred/scared   I'm not _____ of lightning.
7 scraped/scrapped   He _____ the ice off the windscreen.
8 taping/tapping   She was _____ in the last nail.
9 robbed/robed   The shop was _____ on Sunday night.
10 waged/wagged   The dog _____ its tail.

Take up the challenge! •

Complete these words by adding a single or double consonant. Be careful! Some of them do not follow the rule.

(0.5 mark for each correct answer)

ca__age	ha__it	me__al	dra__on	tra__ic
po__ish	fa__ily	stru__le	fo__ow	mo__el
ho__iday	fi__ish	co__y	so__id	pe__y
ca__era	pe__alty	pa__ern	pu__ish	sci__ors

Homophones 1: high-frequency words

 Key idea

Read these two pairs of words:

four   for   eight   ate

They sound the same but they are spelled differently and have different meanings. Words like this are called homophones.

Some of the most common words are homophones. Make sure you choose the right spelling!

Try it out! ●

Correct the mistakes with homophones in this piece of writing. There are ten to find. *(1 mark for each correct answer)*

Eye have bean away from school four too days because my I hurts. I have to where a patch over it. The son is shining and I wish I could go out two play. But I am knot allowed to. I hope I can go back to school won day soon.

Choose the right word to complete each sentence.

(1 mark for each correct answer)

1 there/their   I left it over _____.
2 here/hear   Speak up. I can't _____ you.
3 see/sea   I can't _____ it anywhere.
4 by/bye   I will be back _____ four o'clock.
5 by/buy   I have to _____ a new bag for school.
6 be/bee   I will _____ eight years old tomorrow.
7 know/no   I did not _____ what to do.
8 or/oar   Would you like milk _____ juice?
9 week/weak   I am going on holiday next _____.
10 our/hour   We had to wait an _____ for the train.

Write the word that completes these pairs of homophones.

(1 mark for each correct answer)

new	sum	wood	write	threw
maid	herd	night	seen	way

unit 4

Homophones 2

 Key idea

One of the things that makes spelling tricky is that words that sound the same can be spelled differently. For example:

blew blue   tail tale   piece peace

Pairs of words like this are called homophones. When you are writing you need to be careful to choose the correct spelling.

Try it out! •

Write the word that completes these pairs of homophones.
(0.5 mark for each correct answer)

pair	wait	beech	flour	fir
meet	deer	brake	leek	loan
pain	which	stair	weather	steal
sell	sent	mail	waist	warn

Write the word that the writer should have used.

(1 mark for each correct answer)

1 Goldilocks and the Three Bares.
2 We dug a whole in the garden.
3 We had to toe the car to the garage.
4 Pull the rope and the bell will wring.
5 The children sat in rose for the test.
6 He didn't play fare in that game.
7 I'll rap up the present in shiny paper.
8 I was very board by that film.
9 We are not aloud on the grass when it is wet.
10 The clothes in that shop are very cheep.

Take up the challenge! •

Sometimes there are *three* words that sound the same but are spelled differently! Write two words to complete these sets of homophones. Look out! Sometimes you will need to use words with an apostrophe. *(1 mark for each correct answer)*

rain	soar	sow	heel	bye
rode	cent	their	aisle	to

Verb endings: –s, –ing and –ed

 Key idea

Here are the rules for adding the endings –s, –ed and –ing to verbs:

- verbs ending with a consonant plus y ➔ change y to i and then add –es

  cry   cries   cried

- verbs ending with a short vowel and a single consonant ➔ double the consonant before adding –ed and –ing

  shop   sho**pped**   sho**pping**

- verbs ending in ss, sh, tch, ch, x or zz ➔ add –es rather than –s

  buzz   buzz**es**

  catch   catch**es**

- verbs ending with e ➔ drop the e before adding –ing and –ed
  live   liv**ing**   liv**ed**

Try it out! •

Add the endings –s, –ing and –ed to these verbs.

(0.5 mark for each correct set of three words)

look	change	try	stop	push
slam	copy	use	play	watch
live	trip	miss	open	carry
touch	empty	rub	help	hope

Find and correct the mistakes in this piece of writing. There are twenty. *(0.5 mark for each correct answer)*

"Tell me about what Jack does."

"Well, sometimes he pushs to the front of the line. He likes scareing people by runing at them and stoping just before he bumps into them. He trys to be best at everything. He's always argueing with me. He gets very exciteed. Sometimes in assembly he pinchs people. He likes geting you into trouble. But once he helped me when I triped over."

"And tell me what he did yesterday."

"Lots of bad things. He emptyed juice into the sink. He grabed my pencil just when I was going to start writeing. He copyed my answers. He tickleed me so I startted to laugh in storytime. He driped water all over my painting. He scratchhed his name on the table. He riped a page out of his reading book. Then at home time he cryd when I said I would tell you."

Add –s, –ing and –ed to these verbs ending with l. What patterns can you see? *(0.5 mark for each correct set of three words)*

kneel	label	scowl	expel	peel
quarrel	roll	seal	wail	signal
howl	boil	shovel	tunnel	heal
cancel	pull	patrol	nail	control

unit 6 Verbs with irregular past tenses

 Key idea

The usual way of showing that something happened in the past is to add **–ed** to the verb, for example:

I walk**ed** to school yesterday.

But many common verbs change in other ways.
- swim becomes **swam** (not swimmed)
- sell becomes **sold** (not selled)
- sleep becomes **slept** (not sleeped)

Some verbs follow the same pattern, for example, **grow/grew** and **blow/blew**. But there are no rules. You just have to learn these past tense spellings!

Try it out! ••

Write down the past tense forms of these verbs. Some end with –ed and some do not! *(0.5 mark for each correct answer)*

sit	see	play	take	eat
say	open	tell	come	make
start	run	give	begin	stop
find	hear	know	use	wake

> **ⓘ Top Tip**
> Try putting the verb in a sentence beginning 'Yesterday I ...'

12

Keep practising!

Imagine that you followed this instruction: "Open the door."
Then you could say: "I opened the door." Write what you would
say if you followed these instructions.

(1 mark for each correct answer)

1 Blow out the candles.
2 Stand up.
3 Keep still.
4 Wear your old shoes.
5 Drink your milk.
6 Hold tight.
7 Catch the ball.
8 Feed the cat.
9 Leave the door open.
10 Bring your sun hat to school.

Take up the challenge!

Write down another verb that forms its past tense in the same way
as the verbs below. For example, slide = slid, hide = hid. The last
two are more tricky! *(1 mark for each correct answer)*

slide   tell   creep   ring   find

throw   shake   bend   rise   break

unit 7 Consonant suffixes: –ship, –hood, –ness and –ment

 **Key idea**

The suffixes **–ship**, **–hood**, **–ness** and **–ment** all begin with consonants. They can usually just be added on to the root word:

owner**ship**   false**hood**   kind**ness**   excite**ment**

But if the root word ends with y, change **y** to **i** before adding the suffix:

silly ➜ sill**iness**

likely ➜ likel**ihood**

All words ending with these suffixes are nouns.

Try it out! ●

Add the suffix –ship, –hood, –ness or –ment to these words to make new words. *(1 mark for each correct answer)*

friend	child	enjoy	gentle	embarrass
dark	knight	champion	sad	disappoint

14

Add the suffix –ship, –hood, –ness or –ment to the word so that it makes sense in the sentence. Then rewrite the sentence.
(1 mark for each correct answer)

1	child	Measles is a common _____ illness.
2	leader	She showed great _____ during the game.
3	punish	Your _____ is to stay in at playtime.
4	fierce	The dog's _____ was frightening.
5	improve	There has been a big _____ in your writing.
6	firm	You need to use the brush with more _____.
7	advertise	The new _____ for crisps is very funny.
8	hard	People suffered great _____ crossing the Atlantic.
9	neighbour	There is a new fish and chip shop in our _____.
10	attach	We sent our poems as an e-mail _____.

Add the suffix –hood, –ness or –ment to these words to make ten new words. *(1 mark for each correct answer)*

greedy   sleepy

likely

argue

tidy   accompany

friendly   silly   disembody

!

ALERT

You need to change the spelling first. You can add two of these suffixes to one of the words.

unit 8 Vowel suffixes: –al, –ary and –ic

 Key idea

The suffixes **–al**, **–ary** and **–ic** all begin with vowels. Usually you can just add them on to the root word:

magic**al**   atom**ic**   second**ary**

But if the root word ends with e, drop the **e** before adding the suffix:

nature ➜ natur**al**

And if the root word ends with y, change **y** to **i**:

history ➜ histor**ic**

Try it out! •

Add the suffix –al, –ary or –ic to these words to make new words. *(0.5 mark for each correct answer)*

imagine	music	artist	origin	person
angel	majesty	planet	terrify	centre
rhythm	horrify	sensation	diet	accident
digit	hygiene	revolution	hero	tradition

Write the answers to these clues. All the words end with the suffix –al, –ary or –ic. *(1 mark for each correct answer)*

1   A place where people stay when they are ill.
2   The second month of the year.
3   A person who makes or mends machines.
4   A place where books are kept.
5   The opposite of private.
6   At right angles to a flat surface.
7   A book that explains the meaning and origin of words.
8   A manufactured material that can be moulded into different shapes.
9   When something is normal and not special in any way.
10 Of or in the mind; not written down.

Take up the challenge! •

Write down a word ending with –al, –ary or –ic that is in the same family as these words. For example, drama ➜ dramatic. *(0.5 mark for each correct answer)*

globe	comment	approve	burglar	sympathy
dentist	comedy	volunteer	medicine	use
element	metal	solitude	type	vision
fantasy	add	magician	prime	sign

Verb suffixes: –ate, –en, –ify and –ise

 Key idea

Most words that end with **–ate, –en, –ify** and **–ise** are verbs.

punctu**ate**   sharp**en**   horr**ify**   real**ise**

Sometimes you need to change the spelling of the root word before adding the suffix. Here are the rules:

*   Change final **y** to **i**:
    category = categor**ise**   glory = glor**ify**
*   Drop the final **e**:
    wide = wid**en**   note = not**ify**
*   Double the final consonant if it follows a short vowel sound:
    glad = gla**dden**

So if the word is a verb and it ends with one of these sounds – then you know how it is likely to be spelt!

Try it out! •

Add the suffix –ate, –en, –ify and –ise to turn these adjectives and nouns into verbs. *(0.5 mark for each correct answer)*

tight	critic	class	active	real
vandal	deep	simple	apology	hard
wide	domestic	legal	fertile	sad
pure	oxygen	computer	strength	glory

Write down the verb that is being defined. All the words end in –ate, –en, –ify or –ise. The letter in brackets tells you the first letter of each word. *(1 mark for each correct answer)*

1 To sleep during the winter (h)
2 To make things equal (e)
3 To make something beautiful (b)
4 To make something bright (b)
5 To make someone feel mad (m)
6 To make something work by electricity (e)
7 To leave one country to live in another (e)
8 To make something wide (w)
9 To make something glamorous (g)
10 To copy something (i)

Write down a verb ending with –ate, –ify and –ise that is in the same family as each of these words.

(1 mark for each correct answer)

clear	complex	public	horror	pollen
authority	operation	satisfactory	hypnotism	mystery

Assessment 1

Words with double consonants

Some of the words in these sentences are spelt with one consonant when there should be two. Others are spelt with two consonants when there should be one. Find and correct the mistakes. There are two in each sentence.

(0.25 mark for each correct answer)

1 The rabit hoped away and disappeared in the hedge.
2 We are going to the seaside for a sumer holliday this year.
3 You need to coppy that out again on another piece of papper.
4 The watter in the ketle is beginning to boil.
5 I couldn't finnish my pizza because there was too much peper on it.
6 The King pined the meddal to the soldier's chest.
7 The moddel began to woble and then fell over.
8 I bought four aples and two lemmons.
9 He picked up a hamer and began to batter at the celar door.
10 I cut off a short length of ribon with the scisors.
11 He lives alone in a log cabbin in the midle of the woods.
12 I had spaghetti and sallad for my diner.
13 Hapy Fammilies is my favourite card game.
14 She was punnished for triping people up in the playground.
15 A suden gust of wind blew out the canddle.

Homophones

A **Write the words that sound the same as the words below but are spelt differently and have a different meaning.**

(0.25 mark for each correct answer)

bear	see	no	weak	our
been	sun	won	for	wear

B **The unfinished words in each sentence are homophones. Rewrite the sentences, completing these words.**

(0.5 mark for each correct sentence)

1 He thr_____ a brick thr_____ the window.
2 I w_____ like to go for a walk in the w_____.
3 I he_____ a he_____ of cows mooing in the distance.
4 He ro_____ down the ro_____ on his bike.
5 I hope the cut in my h_____ will h_____ soon.
6 If you a_____ e_____ apples you would feel sick.
7 A strong wind bl_____ the clouds across the bl_____ sky.
8 Tie the k_____ tight so that it does n_____ come undone.
9 He s_____ her a bottle of s_____ for her birthday.
10 You can start to w_____ your stories r_____ away.

Assessment 1 (continued)

Verb endings and irregular verbs

A **Add the endings –s and –ing to these verbs.**
(0.25 mark for each correct answer)

play	tickle	scrub	kiss	carry
touch	stare	reply	bump	chat

B **Fill the gap in each sentence by writing the past tense of the verb.** *(0.25 mark for each correct answer)*

1 start I _____ reading a new book yesterday.
2 run I _____ all the way to school yesterday.
3 wake I _____ up very early yesterday.
4 slam I got in trouble when I _____ the door.
5 find Yesterday I _____ the pen that I had lost.
6 take It _____ Mum two hours to drive to work yesterday.
7 stick I got my head _____ in the railings.
8 buy I _____ some sweets on the way home yesterday.
9 change I _____ my books at the library yesterday.
10 sit I _____ in some wet paint yesterday.

Suffixes

A **Add the suffixes –ment, –ness, –al, –hood, –ship or –ic to the words below.**
(0.25 mark for each correct answer)

amaze	digit	child	atom	dark
friend	rhythm	sad	accident	punish
hero	enjoy	nature	neighbour	history
owner	lonely	argue	centre	happy

B **Write the verbs with these meanings. They end with –ise, –en, -ify or -ate.** *(0.25 mark for each correct answer)*

1 To make something simple.
2 To make something legal.
3 To make something flat.
4 To pause before doing something.
5 To make something deeper.
6 To make something magnetic.
7 To give someone an apology.
8 To make something pure.
9 To use commas and full stops.
10 To make something wider.

Plurals of nouns ending in f and fe

 Key idea

Usually, when you change a noun from singular to plural, the final consonant stays the same. But nouns ending with **f** or **fe** are different.

You change the **f** to **v** and then add **s** or **es**:

calf = cal**ves**   wife = wi**ves**

! ALERT

Words ending in **ff** are exceptions to this rule. You just add an s: sniff = sniffs

! Top Tip

Say the plural word carefully. Do you hear an **f** or a **v** sound at the end? This is a good guide to how the word is spelt.

Try it out! •

This machine makes nouns plural. Write the words that come out. *(1 mark for each correct answer)*

knife loaf skiff elf sheaf half thief sheriff wolf life

Find the spelling mistake in each of these sentences. Rewrite the sentence, putting the mistake right.

(1 mark for each correct answer)

1 I cut the apple into two halfs.
2 People say that cats have nine lifes.
3 The wolf gave two big puves and blew the house down.
4 In autumn the leafes begin to fall off the trees.
5 The path along the top of the clives was dangerous.
6 Every afternoon we read quietly to ourselfs.
7 I got my shirt cuffes covered in paint.
8 The book shelfs in my bedroom are full.
9 Young cows are called calvs.
10 They organised the party all by themselfes.

Take up the challenge! •

Write the plural forms of these nouns. Some of them do not follow the usual rule. Some of them can be spelt in two different ways. *(1 mark for each correct answer)*

belief   chef   roof   ruff   dwarf   gulf
safe (to keep money in)   scarf   wolf   hoof

Common endings: –ight and –ough

 **Key idea**

Say these words: **fight, kite.** They rhyme. The letter string **–ight** always has this sound when it comes after a consonant and is at the end of a word.

The ending **–ough** is more tricky! It has many different sounds. You can hear three of these in the words **cough, though** and **bough.** You have to learn the words that end with this letter string.

Try it out! •

Add the ending –ight, –ite, –ow or –ough to these beginnings to make words. *(1 mark for each correct answer)*

    alth   qu   fr   exc   en   c   del   sn   midn   tr

add.....
-ight
-ite
-ow
-ough

c

cough

Fill the gaps with a word ending in –ight or –ough.

(1 mark for each correct answer)

1 This piece of meat is too _____ to eat.
2 Our _____ for Spain takes off at nine o'clock.
3 It's getting dark. Turn on the _____.
4 The farmer has to _____ the ground before planting seeds.
5 He said he _____ be back at school tomorrow.
6 We are not allowed to play _____ games in the playground.
7 The _____ raised his sword and charged into battle.
8 The farmer filled the _____ with food for the pigs.
9 He sat on the highest _____ of the tree.
10 If you have poor _____ you need glasses.

Take up the challenge! •

Write a word ending in –ough that rhymes with each of these words. *(2 marks for each correct answer)*

1 rough
2 bough
3 trough
4 dough

5 **Now write a word ending in –ough that has no rhymes!**
   (2 marks for the correct answer)

Common endings: –tion, –ious and –ial

 Key idea

Many words end with the suffixes **-tion**, **-ious** and **-ial**.

instruc**tion**   cons**cious**   spec**ial**

Notice how all three suffixes start with a **sh** sound.

In some words, such as obv**ious**, the **-ious** suffix is pronounced differently and has two syllables.

Words ending in **-tion** are nouns. Words ending in **-ious** and **-ial** are adjectives.

Try it out! ·

Add the suffix –tion, –ious or –ial to these root words to make new words. *(1 mark for each correct answer)*

subtract	fury	elect	proverb	prevent
finance	create	exhaust	envy	construct
victory	decorate	mystery	sacrifice	electrocute

!

ALERT

If the root word ends with e or y, you will need to change its spelling first.

tion

ious

ial

Write the words that match the definitions. They all end with –tion, –ious or –ial. The first letters give you a clue.

(1 mark for each correct answer)

1 cu   wanting to find out about things
2 in   first; at the beginning
3 fr   a number that is not a whole number
4 hib   the long sleep that some animals have in winter
5 del   tasting very good
6 ca   the writing that goes with a picture
7 art   not natural; made by human beings
8 pre   very valuable
9 exc   something that does not follow the rules
10 illus   a picture in a book

Write a word ending with –tion, –ious or –ial that belongs in the same family as these words. *(0.5 mark for each correct answer)*

compete   suspect   destroy   anxiety   society
religion   produce   palace   explain   face

Prefixes: a–, al–, ad– and af–

 Key idea

An interesting group of words begins with the prefixes **a–**, **al–**, **ad–** and **af–**:

   apart   **al**most   **ad**verb   **af**flict

Notice that the first sound is not the same in all these words, and that often it does not have the usual "a" sound. Knowing that these prefixes all begin with the letter **a** will help you remember how to spell them. The prefix **al–** means **all**, but it has only one **l**.

Try it out! •

Add the prefix a–, al– or ad– to these endings to make words that fit in the gaps. Write the words in your book.

(1 mark for each correct answer)

I sat up in bed and looked at the clock. It was __most three o'clock. I was wide __wake. I threw the blankets __side, jumped out of bed, and got dressed. I picked up the bag that I had __ready packed and opened the door. I tiptoed __cross the landing and downstairs. __though I knew that everyone in the house was fast __sleep, I did not make a sound. The front door __ways made a loud squeaking noise, so I went out of the back door. There was no one to be seen. I walked __way from the house as quickly as I could. My big __venture was about to begin.

Write the word that is being defined. They all begin with the prefixes a–, al–, ad– or af–. *(1 mark for each correct answer)*

1 A word that adds to the meaning of a noun.
2 Similar; the same as each other.
3 In or going to another country.
4 Kind and loving.
5 To let someone in.
6 In a voice that can be heard.
7 To think something or someone is very good.
8 On fire.
9 Having total power over everything.
10 Rich; wealthy.

Take up the challenge! •

Add the prefixes a–, al–, ad– or af– to these endings to make words. Some of the words are uncommon or old-fashioned. Check their meanings in a good dictionary.

(0.5 mark for each correct answer)

–ford	–firm	–join	–front
–float	–ground	–bide	–ways
–just	–fix	–right	–so
–together	–hesive	–ware	–opt
–loft	–fresh	–vent	–vantage

a   ad
al   af

Assessment 2

Plurals of nouns ending in f and fe

Write the plural noun that fits in the gap.

(1 mark for each correct answer)

1   roof   Three _____ in our street were damaged in the storm.

2   shelf   Mum put up two more _____ for my books.

3   leaf   We made patterns out of dried _____.

4   cliff   A line of _____ rises up from the beach.

5   chef   Four _____ work in the kitchens.

6   knife   They always keep their _____ sharp.

7   wolf   A long time ago there were _____ in the British Isles.

8   safe   The manager saw that all the _____ had been forced open.

9   thief   _____ had broken into the bank during the night.

10 puff   It took me three _____ to blow out my candles.

Common endings: –ight and –ough

Find the ten spelling mistakes and put them right.

(1 mark for each correct answer)

1   He's been coffing all nite.

2   I'm fritened of litning.

3   It's not quight brite enouf to see the picture clearly.

4   I miht be late back tonit.

5   I don't like doenuts.

Common endings: –tion, –ious and –ial

Add the ending –tion, –ious or –ial to these words to make new words. *(0.5 mark for each correct answer)*

race	evaporate	fury	substitute	mystery
exhibit	grace	react	dictator	illustrate

Prefixes a–, al–, ad– and af–

Find the five spelling mistakes and put them right.

(1 mark for each correct answer)

1 I was allmost late for school.
2 The word "quickly" is an addverb.
3 The word "beautiful" is an ajjective.
4 The dog next door is very afectionate.
5 The ship stayed affloat after hitting the rocks.

Investigating letters: k, v and q

 Key idea

Letters do not just pop up all over the place in words. They combine only with certain letters and appear at only certain places in a word.

- k is usually followed by the vowels **e** and **i**. The only consonants that come before k are **c, l, n, s** and **r**.

- v is always followed by a vowel. No words end with v. The only consonants that come before v are **r, n, l** and **d**.

- q is always followed by the letter **u**, and then another vowel. Words end with **que**, but not with **qu**. The only consonant that comes before q at the start of a word is **s**.

Knowing these patterns will help you spell words correctly.

Try it out! ·

Rearrange the letters to make words.

(0.5 mark for each correct answer)

ttelke	nav	efiv	diliqu
misk	uqcki	telekson	canolov
laque	brev	kashe	kawe
qeesuze	verri	etik	ecovr
krow	eequn	ravtel	kilm

Write the word that matches the definition. They all include the letters k, v or q. *(1 mark for each correct answer)*

1 The edge of the pavement.
2 A colour of the rainbow.
3 The noise that ducks make.
4 Part of a poem or song.
5 An animal with a bushy tail that lives in trees.
6 Part of your foot where it joins the leg.
7 The same in amount or size.
8 To go from one place to another.
9 To make or discover something
 for the first time.
10 The opposite of strong.

The words in the lists below are nonsense words. However, the words in each list do stick to the rules for k, v and q – except for one! Write down the word in each list that is not a possible word in the English language. *(2 marks for each correct answer)*

1 nork	sheq	bick	neek
2 feeck	nack	merve	dilver
3 nove	vome	griv	maver
4 turve	bonvent	vam	cavto
5 quib	qale	blique	squin

Write an explanation of why they are impossible words.

Investigating letter strings: wa, wo, ss, sc and ch

 Key idea

Like individual letters, letter strings do not pop up just anywhere in words. They appear at certain positions and with certain other letters.

- wa and wo almost always come at the beginning of words. The only exception is the word "two". When they come in the middle of a word, s usually comes before them.
- ss comes in the middle and at the end of words, but never at the beginning. There is always a vowel before it and after it.
- sc is usually found at the beginning of words and sometimes in the middle, but not at the end – except for the modern word disc!
- ch comes at the beginning, middle and end of words. There is always a vowel before it and after it – unless it is part of the letter string tch.

Try it out! . . . .

The letter strings wa, wo, ss, sc and ch have been left out of these words. Add the correct letters, and write the complete word. *(0.5 mark for each correct answer)*

___rld	bran___	dre___	___ooter	e___o
expre___ion	s___llow	___bble	swit___	___ratch
___ange	le___on	s___llen	bi___uit	___aracter
___reen	___sh	___od	___lk	___ter

36

Keep practising! ●

Write the word that is being defined. They all include the letter strings wa, wo, ss, sc or ch. *(1 mark for each correct answer)*

1 The thick hair of sheep.
2 People, usually men, keep their money in this.
3 A lawn is made out of this.
4 A piece of cloth worn around the neck.
5 A piece of furniture for sitting on.
6 A group of people singing together.
7 A large group of bees moving together.
8 A white bird with a long, thin neck.
9 A meeting when everyone in a school
   gathers together for prayers and notices.
10 A moving stairway.

Take up the challenge! ●

Make words by adding two of the letter strings wa, wo, ss, sc and ch to these sets of letters. For two of the words, you will need to add the same letter string twice.

(1 mark for each correct answer)

1	t	6	iors
2	ur	7	rat
3	or	8	diuion
4	ree	9	poeion
5	ildle	10	eerfulne

Same letters, different sound 1: ou, au and ow

Key idea

One of the reasons why spelling is tricky is that many letter strings can be pronounced in different ways. Listen to the sounds that **ou**, **au** and **ow** make in these words.

ou	round	group	young	would
au	August	sausage	laugh	
ow	now	snow		

You need to learn the different sounds that these letter strings make. Some are much more common than others, and some come only at particular places in words.

Try it out! ●

Sort these words according to the sounds that the letter strings ou, au and ow make. There are six groups, with three words in each, and two odd words left over!

(0.5 mark for each word you put in the correct group)

south	group	drown	snow	could
soup	saucer	allow	bounce	throw
because	trouble	route	cousin	thousand
pillow	touch	autumn	flower	cause

The answer to each clue is a word that rhymes with the word in bold but has a different letter string for the vowel sound.

(1 mark for each correct answer)

1 **sung**   the opposite of old
2 **short**   criminals go on trial here
3 **hoop**   a liquid food
4 **shower**   the opposite of sweet
5 **go**   the opposite of quick
6 **crown**   the kind of word that names something
7 **hole**   a deep, round dish
8 **flower**   sixty minutes
9 **bubble**   twice as many
10 **jaws**   what makes something happen; the reason

Take up the challenge! •

Write the word that completes these pairs of homophones. They all include the letter string ou, au or ow.

(1 mark for each correct answer)

| 1 paws | 3 flower | 5 fowl | 7 no | 9 wood |
| 2 ant | 4 aloud | 6 toe | 8 root | 10 coarse |

Same letters, different sound 2: ar, or, ear and our

 Key idea

Letter strings with vowels and the letter **r** can be pronounced in many different ways. Some are more common than others, and some come only at certain positions in words.

- **ar** as in **farm** is most common
  ar as in **warm** follows only the letters **w** or **qu**
  ar as in **grammar** comes only at the end of words – or before final letter **d**, as in wizard
- **or** as in **horse** is most common
  or as in **work** comes only after the letter **w**
  or as in **doctor** comes only at the end of words
- **ear** as in **year** is most common
  ear as in **bear** comes only at the end of words
  ear as in **learn** comes only at the beginning or in the middle of words
- **our** as in **your** has one syllable
  our as in **sour** has two syllables and comes only at the end of words
  our as in **colour** comes only at the end

Try it out! ●

Sort these words into pairs in which the letter strings ar, or, ear and our have the same sound. *(1 mark for each correct pair of words)*

harbour	pear	motor	burglar	beard	card
worst	earn	sour	four	sport	backwards
lizard	mirror	wear	shark	torch	neighbour
quarter	worth	heard	our	clear	course

Fill the gap in each word by adding the letter string ar, or, ear or our. Write the words in your book.

(0.5 mark for each correct answer)

1   He p_____ed water carefully into the j_____.
2   My fav_____ite auth_____ is Jacqueline Wilson.
3   W_____ms can tunnel through the _____th.
4   The al_____m goes off at qu_____ter past seven.
5   I used to love the st_____y of Goldilocks and the Three B_____s.
6   Knights carried a sp_____ and wore arm_____.
7   The visit_____ stayed only for an h_____.
8   I found a big green caterpill_____ this m_____ning.

Write a word that rhymes and includes the letter string in bold.

(1 mark for each correct answer)

1	cart	**ear**	6	earth	**or**
2	pour	**ar**	7	turn	**ear**
3	short	**our**	8	shorter	**ar**
4	heard	**or**	9	born	**our**
5	farmer	**our**	10	word	**ear**

41

unit 20

Same letters, different sound 3: igh, augh and ough

 Key idea

The letter string **gh** is tricky. Sometimes it is part of a vowel sound.

- Following the letter **i**, it always makes the long i phoneme: **high, fight.**
- Following the letter string **ei**, it usually makes the long a phoneme: **weigh, eight.** But height is an exception!
- Following the letter string **au**, it usually makes the vowel phoneme you can hear in the word **caught.**
- Following the letter string **ou**, it makes many different vowel sounds: **bough, though, through, fought.**

And sometimes **gh** sounds like the consonant f: **enough, trough, laugh.**

Try it out! •

Sort these words into ten groups: eight rhyming pairs and two words that do not rhyme with any of the others.

(1 mark for each correct answer)

delight	dough	freight	cough	although
laughter	naughty	sight	tough	sigh
trough	taught	thigh	weight	
enough	daughter	haughty	caught	

42

Write the word that answers the clue. They all include the letters strings igh, augh or ough. *(1 mark for each correct answer)*

1 The opposite of loose.
2 The sound that a horse makes.
3 The opposite of low.
4 The opposite of son.
5 The opposite of sold.
6 The opposite of smooth.
7 The opposite of dull.
8 The past tense of think.
9 The past tense of catch.
10 The opposite of left.

Take up the challenge! ·····················

Write a word that sounds the same but is spelt differently. They all include the letter strings igh, augh or ough.

(1 mark for each correct answer)

1 site	6 draft
2 wait	7 doe
3 threw	8 slay
4 ruff	9 taut
5 mite	10 ate

Words with common roots

 Key idea

Many words include roots or parts that you find in many other words as well. For example, all these words include the root **tri-**, which means three:

triangle   triple   trio   tricycle   tripod

And these words include the root **sign**, which comes from the Latin word "signum" which meant "mark":

design   signal   sign   signature

Notice that this root is pronounced in two different ways.

Try it out! •

Make twenty words by combining roots in the circle on the left with roots in the circle on the right. You will need to use some of the roots more than once. *(0.5 mark for each correct answer)*

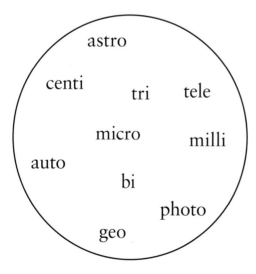

astro
centi
tri   tele
micro   milli
auto
bi
photo
geo

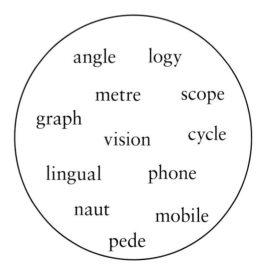

angle   logy
metre   scope
graph
vision   cycle
lingual   phone
naut
mobile
pede

Write the word that is being defined.

(1 mark for each correct answer)

1 (noun) an instrument for measuring temperature
2 (noun) a text written by hand, rather than printed
3 (adjective) without end; too big to be measured
4 (adjective) having four sides of equal length
5 (noun) an imaginary animal with one horn
6 (noun) a long speech by one person
7 (noun) the story of a person's life, written by someone else
8 (noun) a bridge that carries water across a valley
9 (noun) the study of animals
10 (noun) any animal with four legs

Write three words including each of these roots.

(1 mark for each correct answer)

1 equ (equal)
2 port (to carry)
3 ped (foot)
4 sim (the same)
5 uni (one)
6 graph (writing)
7 phon (sound)
8 tele (far, at a distance)
9 hydr (water)
10 auto (self)

> **! Top Tip**
> You could look
> in a dictionary if
> you get stuck.

Dictionary

Extending words

 **Key idea**

Many words can be extended by adding on suffixes.

create ➔ creation ➔ creative

art ➔ artist ➔ artistic ➔ artistically ➔ artful ➔ artfully

Remember! Sometimes you need to change the spelling of the root word before adding the suffix. Two important rules are:

* drop the final **e** before adding suffixes beginning with a vowel:
  relate   relative
* change **y** to **i** before adding the suffix:
  beauty   beautiful
  terrify   terrific

Try it out! ●

Add one of the suffixes in the list to extend the root words.
(0.5 mark for each correct answer)

–ful   –ly   –ive   –tion   –ic   –ist

novel	thought	greedy	mass	exhibit
history	rhythm	piano	wonder	gentle
slow	starve	angel	mercy	expense
hope	shocking	subtract	hygiene	cycle

Add one of the suffixes in the list to the words in bold so that they fit in the sentence. Sometimes you need to change the spelling of the word first. *(0.5 mark for each correct answer)*

–ful   –ly   –ive   –tion   –ic   –ist

1 The painting was very **colour** and **realist**.
2 He walked **quick** away in the wrong **direct**.
3 The **instinct react** when you touch something hot is to move your hand away as fast as you can.
4 The **science** was carrying out an **investigate** into global warming.
5 The poor dog was in a **pity** state when the police **eventual** found it.
6 There'll be more **horror** accidents on that road if people don't drive more **careful**.
7 The **cartoon** drew a face with a big **attract** smile.
8 We talked about the most **effect** ways of reducing **pollute**.
9 The **tour** was **hopeless** lost in the narrow streets of the old city.
10 The **detect** used **photograph** evidence to track down the criminal.

Take up the challenge! •

Make two words by adding the suffixes in the list to these words. You can add more than one suffix at a time, for example:
    real + –ist + –ic = realistic
(0.5 mark for each word you make and spell correctly)

–ful   –ly   –ive   –tion   –ic   –ist

1 attract   3 imagine   5 colour   7 science   9 drama
2 correct   4 relate   6 invent   8 explode   10 terror

unit 23

Suffixes: -able and -ible

 **Key idea**

Many adjectives end with the suffix **–able** or **–ible**:

breakable   possible

Spelling these words is tricky because **–able** and **–ible** sound the same. There is no rule about which suffix to use, but there are some helpful patterns:

- –able endings are much more common than –ible endings.
- If the first part of the adjective is a word in itself, then the suffix is usually –able (as in **breakable** and **reasonable**).
- If the consonant before the suffix is **s**, then it is usually –ible.

When adding –able and –ible to root words, you need to follow the usual spelling rules:

- change final **y** to **i**
  justify = justifiable
- drop the final **e**
  excuse = excusable

BUT NOT when the final consonant is **soft c** or **g**. There are other exceptions to this rule too!

Try it out! •

Add the suffix **–able** or **–ible** to these words to make adjectives. Sometimes you need to change the spelling first.

(0.5 mark for each correct answer)

suit	comfort	resist	drink	love
value	rely	collapse	predict	access
contempt	renew	vary	reverse	believe
fashion	sense	excite	forgive	use

Write down the adjective ending –able or –ible that fits in the gaps in these sentences. You need to use the word in bold.

(1 mark for each correct answer)

1 If you can **understand** something, it is und_____.
2 If something **horrifies** you, it is horr_____.
3 If you can **avoid** something, it is av_____.
4 Something you **envy** is env_____.
5 Something you **admire** is adm_____.
6 If you cannot **digest** something, it is indig_____.
7 If you can **inflate** something, it is infl_____.
8 Something that fills you with **terror** is terr_____.
9 Something you cannot **deny** is unden_____.
10 Something you cannot **describe** is indescr_____.

ALERT

There is something unusual about how all the root words change when you do this.

Take up the challenge! • • • • • • • • • • • •

Write the adjectives ending with –able or –ible that belong in the same family as these root words. *(0.5 mark for each correct answer)*

notice	hug	forget	divide	irritate
appreciate	agree	like	force	name
comprehend	foresee	share	despise	regret
peace	neglect	replace	permit	change

Suffixes: –tion and –sion

 **Key idea**

The suffixes **–tion** and **–sion** turn verbs into nouns.

operate = operation   confuse = confusion

Spelling these words is tricky because –tion and –sion sound the same. There is no rule about which suffix to use, but there are some helpful patterns:

- Words ending in –tion are much more common than words ending in –sion.
- If the root verb ends with the letters **te** or **t** then the suffix is usually –tion.
- The suffix –tion often follows the letter **a** to make the ending **-ation**, in words like **imagination**.
- If the root verb ends with the letters **d**, **de**, **s**, **ss** or **se** then the suffix is usually –sion.

Try it out! ·

Add the suffix –tion or –sion to these verbs to make nouns.

(0.5 mark for each correct answer)

create	exhaust	revise	expand
pollute	vary	possess	indicate
include	decide	predict	illustrate
starve	explode	relax	explore
suspend	prevent	impress	invade

ALERT

Sometimes you will need to change the spelling of the verb first.

Write the word that fits in the gap in each sentence. They all end with –tion or –sion. The first letters are given as a clue.

(1 mark for each correct answer)

1 Sub_____ is the opposite of addition.
2 Div_____ is the opposite of multiplication.
3 She won first prize in a tap dance comp_____.
4 We had a long disc_____ about experiments on animals.
5 Coop_____ is another word for working together.
6 He needed a blood transf_____ after the accident.
7 I got a good mark for the compr_____ test.
8 The police moved the car because it was causing an obstr_____.
9 The inv_____ of printing meant that books could be produced much more quickly.
10 Drums and rattles are perc_____ instruments.

Take up the challenge! ●

Turn these verbs into nouns ending with –tion or –sion. You will need to change the spelling of the verb first (and sometimes not just the last letter). *(0.5 mark for each correct answer)*

qualify	cancel	attend	deceive	compel
reduce	expel	suck	explain	solve
produce	admit	prescribe	define	recognise
imagine	permit	evolve	pronounce	describe

Compound words

 Key idea

Many words in English are made up of two separate words joined together.

fire/works   water/proof   light/house   tooth/paste

Knowing this makes these long words easier to spell because you can divide them up into two parts.

Try it out!

Join up these words to make twenty compound words. Use each word only once. *(0.5 mark for each correct answer)*

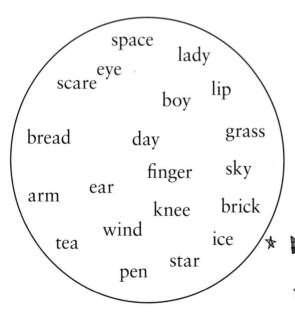

space   lady
eye
scare   lip
boy
bread   day   grass
finger   sky
arm   ear
knee   brick
wind
tea   ice
pen   star

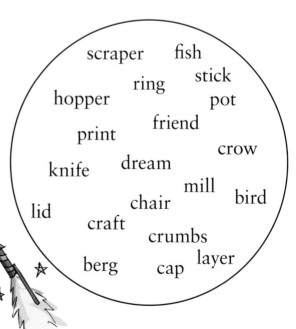

scraper   fish
ring   stick
hopper   pot
print   friend
crow
knife   dream
mill   bird
chair
lid   craft
crumbs
berg   cap   layer

Rewrite this story, adding the missing part of the compound words. (*1 mark for each correct answer*)

Today I woke up early. I was nervous and worried that I might _____sleep. There was just one thought in my mind: Today is the day of the big game. I am the goal_____ for our local _____ball team, and this _____noon we are playing in the final. I looked out of my bed_____ window. It was pouring. "Oh, no!" I thought. "We'll be playing in mud! Never mind." I rushed down_____ and had a good break_____. By the time I had finished, the rain had stopped and there was a bright _____bow in the sky. I wondered what would happen. Maybe I would make a fantastic save in the last minute to win the game. And maybe the _____line in the news_____ would read: Brilliant Keeper Saves the Day.

Write down the word that goes after the first word and in front of the second word to make a pair of compound words.

(*1 mark for each correct answer*)

For example:

guide + **book** = guidebook

book + mark = bookmark

1 bird, room
2 head, house
3 sea, ways
4 birth, light
5 time, cloth

6 flower, room
7 water, read
8 hand, pipes
9 green, work
10 sand, back

unit 26
It's and its

Key idea

The words it's and its are the same apart from the apostrophe. People sometimes use one when they should use the other.

- **Its** is a possessive pronoun. It shows that one thing belongs to another. Put the kitten back in **its** basket now, please.
- **It's** is short for **it is** (or **it has**). The apostrophe shows where the i of is (or the **ha** of has) has been left out.
  It's (it is) a long way back to the car park.
  It's (it has) been a long time.

To check which word you need, see if you can use **it is** (or **it has**) instead. If you can, then you need **it's**!

Try it out!

Write the word that fits in the gap in the answers to these questions. Is it it's or its? *(1 mark for each correct answer)*

1 What time is it? ___ four o'clock.
2 How does an elephant pick things up? With ___ trunk.
3 Where's my hat? ___ hanging on the peg by the door.
4 Why are you taking that T-shirt back to the shop? Because ___ too big.
5 What does a horse use to keep flies away? ___ tail.
6 Is it a bird? No, ___ Superman!
7 Why isn't that clock working? Because ___ hands are stuck.
8 How should you pick up a dog? NOT by ___ ears!
9 What's the matter with your soup? ___ cold.
10 How many wheels does that lorry have? ___ got twelve.

The words it's and its have been left out of this story. Rewrite it, adding the correct word in each gap.
(1 mark for each correct answer)

___ now two days since the monster came down into the village from __ cave in the mountain. At the time, I was high up on the church tower mending the clock. The first I knew about it was when I heard someone call out: "___ coming! The monster is coming!" Then I heard the thud of ___ great feet and felt the ground shake. Everyone else ran inside and hid. So I am the only person who got a good look at the monster. ___ a kind of dragon. ___ back is covered with sharp spikes. ___ eyes glow red like two pieces of coal in the fire. ___ able to blow fire from ___ mouth. ___ frightening to think what would happen if you got in the way of one of those blasts.

There are ten mistakes with it's and its in these sentences. Rewrite them, correcting the mistakes.
(1 mark for each correct answer)

1 That bike! Its the second time its chain has got stuck.
2 You can tell from it's rhythm that it's by the same poet.
3 Its' the shape that gives this new sports car it's appeal.
4 The island was once known for it's natural beauty and its peace and quiet. But its a noisy and polluted place now.
5 What a clever dog! It's found it's own way back home.
6 Look at that ghost! Its carrying its head under it's arm!
7 I love football. At it's best, it's the greatest game in the world.

unit 27

Assessment 3

Same letters, different sounds: ar, or, ear, our; igh, augh, ough

A Sort these words into groups in which the letter strings ar, or, ear, our, igh, augh and ough have the same sound. There are twelve groups of two or three words.

(0.25 mark for each correct group of words)

pear	draughty	word	your	bough	chorus
reward	taught	flour	bear	learn	garden
plough	naughty	portrait	pearl	pour	laughter
wear	swarm	dough	farm	quarter	sword
our	although	hour	court	army	worm
search	worship				

B Write the words that answer the clues.
They all include the letter strings ar, or, ear, our, augh or ough.
The first letter is given to help you.

(0.25 mark for each correct answer)

1 The opposite of late (e).
2 The opposite of better (w).
3 The opposite of remember (f).
4 The opposite of cool (w).
5 The opposite of soft (h).
6 The opposite of sweet (s).
7 The opposite of son (d).
8 The opposite of smooth (r).

Words with common roots

Complete the word being defined by adding a common root.
(0.5 mark for each correct answer)

1 Any animal with four legs. _____ruped
2 To send goods to be sold in another country. ex_____
3 Flat and round in shape. _____ular
4 Someone who walks. _____estrian
5 An insect said to have a hundred legs. _____ipede
6 A vehicle with pedals and three wheels. _____cycle
7 A device for talking with people who are far away. _____phone
8 A device for seeing things that are very small. micro_____
9 A device for measuring temperature. thermo_____
10 The fear of spiders. arachno_____

Extending words

Extend these words by adding the suffix –ful, –ly, –ive, –ic or –ist.
(0.25 mark for each correct answer)

hope	novel	horrible	hygiene	attract
careful	history	tour	greedy	invent
pain	violin	expense	total	create
beauty	artist	pity	piano	rhythm

Assessment 3 *(continued)*

Suffixes: –able, –ible, –tion and –sion

A Change these words by adding the suffix –able, –ible, –tion or –sion. *(0.25 mark for each correct answer)*

enjoy   collide   collapse   correct

notice   expand   pollute   digest

justify   confuse   decorate   sense

B **Write the words being defined. They all end with the suffix –able, –ible, –tion or –sion. The initial letter gives you a clue.** *(0.25 mark for each correct answer)*

1 worth a lot of money; important (v)
2 that you can trust or depend on (r)
3 easy to see (v)
4 hard to believe (i)
5 a note asking someone to attend an event, especially a party (i)
6 explanation of the meaning of a word (d)
7 the ending of something (c)
8 talk amongst a group of people (d)

Please come to my party on Saturday, 10 July at 6pm

Fancy Dress!

Compound words

Join up these forty words to make twenty compound words.
(0.25 mark for each correct answer)

birth
sauce   fire
tooth
lamp   snow
pop   sea   bed
flower
goal   head
light
air   eye
foot   hand
sun
water
play

day
ground
keeper
bag   corn
brush   craft
ache
brow
shade   house
print   flake
room   works
side   rise   fall
pan
pot

It's and its

Write it's or its in the gaps. *(0.5 mark for each correct answer)*

Look! There's a bird in the ivy.

Yes. I think ___ a wren. ___ one of the smallest birds in this country.

Where do you think ___ nest is?

Probably low down in a hole in the wall. The male bird makes the nest and then ___ lined with feathers by the female. The nest is unusual. ___ got a round shape like a dome.

What does the wren eat?

___ main food is insects and spiders.

Is it a rare bird?

No ___ one of the most common British birds.

Does it sing?

Not really. ___ song, if you can call it that, is a sort of dry rattling noise. But ___ very loud.

Look! There it is again! You can see ___ little sticking-up tail.

Word lists

Unit 2: Words with double consonants

rabbit	scruffy	yellow	happen	possible
bubble	traffic	balloon	puppy	assembly
rubbish	raffle	summer	apple	bottle
cabbage	toffee	hammer	opposite	letter
hobby	giggle	drummer	carry	rattle
riddle	dagger	common	borrow	butter
sudden	juggle	funny	mirror	kettle
ladder	soggy	dinner	hurry	puzzle
wedding	pillow	tennis	berry	dazzle
muddle	umbrella	manners	lesson	
different	collect	connect	scissors	

Unit 3: Homophones 1: high-frequency words

there/their	some/sum	for/four
to/too/two	would/wood	eight/ate
where/wear	sun/son	not/knot
here/hear	be/bee	our/hour
see/sea	week/weak	way/weigh
been/bean	no/know	seen/scene
by/buy/bye	write/right	heard/herd
new/knew	through/threw	night/knight
one/won	I/eye	

Unit 4: Homophones 2

pair/pear	stare/stair	toe/tow	peace/piece
beech/beach	weather/	ring/wring	plain/plane
flower/flour	whether	rap/wrap	prey/pray
meet/meat	steel/steal	blue/blew	rain/rein/reign
dear/deer	sell/cell	great/grate	bow/bough
break/brake	waist/waste	main/mane	hole/whole
pain/pane	bare/bear	pale/pail	root/route
which/witch	hole/whole	peek/peak	heel/heal

Unit 5: Verb endings: –s, –ing and –ed

ending with a consonant + y	ending with a short vowel and one consonant	ending with ss, sh, tch, ch, x, zz	ending with e
tries/tried	hopping/ hopped	misses	smiling/smiled
carries/carried	clapping/ clapped	kisses	hoping/hoped
replies/replied	rubbing/rubbed	crashes	tickling/tickled
copies/copied	stopping/ stopped	pushes	using/used
empties/ emptied	begging/begged	wishes	inviting/invited
worries/worried	humming/ hummed	scratches	arguing/argued
	stepping/ stepped	itches	
	wrapping/ wrapped	pinches	
		teaches	
		fixes	
		mixes	
		buzzes	
		fizzes	

Unit 6: Verbs with irregular past tenses

high-frequency
words
sit/sat
see/saw
take/took
eat/ate
say/said
tell/told
come/came
make/made
run/ran
give/gave

begin/began
find/found
hear/heard
know/knew
wake/woke
go/went
get/got

other words
catch/caught
teach/taught
think/thought
buy/bought
drink/drank
stick/stuck
sing/sang
blow/blew
draw/drew
grow/grew
throw/threw

write/wrote
drive/drove
break/broke
hold/held
sell/sold
sleep/slept
keep/kept
leave/left
wear/wore
bite/bit
hide/hid
fall/fell

Unit 7: Consonant suffixes: –ship, –hood, –ness and –ment

–ship
friendship
hardship
membership
championship
leadership
ownership
partnership

–hood
childhood
neighbourhood
fatherhood
motherhood
boyhood
girlhood
falsehood

–ment
equipment
enjoyment
statement
announcement
argument
excitement
agreement
disappointment
amazement
government
punishment

–ness
darkness
gentleness
sadness
greatness
kindness
softness
carelessness
forgetfulness
happiness
laziness
loneliness
greediness
friendliness
foolishness

Unit 8: Vowel suffixes: –al, –ary and –ic

–al	–ary	–ic
personal	secondary	atomic
digital	primary	rhythmic
musical	dictionary	artistic
magical	necessary	heroic
traditional	ordinary	angelic
seasonal	imaginary	terrific
normal	library	majestic
national	anniversary	historic
original	secretary	hygienic
natural	vocabulary	basic
central		metallic

Unit 9: Verb suffixes: –ate, –en, –ify and –ise

–ate	–en	–ify	–ise
create	sharpen	classify	magnetise
educate	soften	solidify	computerise
decorate	strengthen	purify	visualise
punctuate	deafen	simplify	globalise
calculate	darken	horrify	realise
concentrate	tighten	mystify	criticise
elasticate	loosen	electrify	glamorise
medicate	widen	magnify	vandalise
complicate	sadden	clarify	apologise
activate	flatten	qualify	categorise
pollinate	madden		fertilise

Unit 11: Plurals of nouns ending in f and fe

ending in f or fe (change to ves)	ending in ff (just add s)	exceptions
calf/calves	puff/puffs	belief/beliefs
half/halves	sniff/sniffs	chef/chefs
leaf/leaves	cuff/cuffs	reef/reefs
loaf/loaves	cliff/cliffs	chief/chiefs
shelf/shelves		handkerchief/
wolf/wolves		handkerchiefs or
elf/elves		handkerchieves
knife/knives		roof/roofs
wife/wives		safe/safes
life/lives		

Unit 12: Common endings: –ight and –ough

ending in –ough		ending in –ight	
enough	cough	light	tight
rough	trough	right	sight
tough	though	might	flight
bough	dough	night	delight
plough	through	fight	bright
	thorough		

Unit 13: Common endings: –tion, –ious, and –ial

ending in –tion
action
subtraction
construction
election
correction
exhaustion
prediction
invention
definition

pollution
education
creation
illustration
decoration
imagination
organisation
invitation
desperation
occupation

ending in –ious (one syllable)
infectious
suspicious
delicious
religious
anxious
conscious
ferocious
precious

ending in –ious (two syllables)
curious
obvious
serious
furious
previous
mysterious
various
envious
victorious

ending in –ial (one syllable)
special
official
social
artificial
initial
essential
influential
commercial
controversial

ending in –ial (two syllables)
material
aerial
industrial
terrestrial
proverbial
dictatorial

Unit 14: Prefixes a–, al–, ad– and af–

prefix a–		prefix al–	prefix ad–	prefix af–
	alike			
away	ahead	almost	adjective	affix
asleep	alive	already	adverb	affront
awake	apart	always	admire	affection
alight	aloft	almighty	adventure	affluent
along	afloat	although	advertise	afflict
aloud	ablaze	altogether	admit	affirm
aside			adjust	
			advance	

Unit 16: Investigating letters: k, v and q

v at the beginning		v in the middle		v at the end
	vowel		removal	
	vest		invent	no words
van	visit	river	revolve	end with v
view	vegetable	travel	silver	
village		clever	nerve	
		sleeve	servant	
		above		

k at the beginning		k in the middle	k at the end	
	kerb			talk
	know			milk
king	knife	brake	back	sink
kitchen	kangaroo	joke	sock	bank
kite	koala	like	stick	fork
kettle	karate	crackle	check	peek
keep	kung fu	bucket	tuck	weak
		chicken		
		wrinkle		
		ankle		

			square	liquid
			squabble	conquer
quick	quarrel	squeak	equal	antique
question		squirrel	equipment	unique
quarter		squeeze	aquarium	mosque
	queen			
	quote			

Unit 17: Investigating letter strings:
wa, wo, ss, sc and ch

wait	swan	no words	wobble	sword	two
wall	sway	end with	woman	swollen	
wash	swallow	wa	worm	swore	
waggle	reward		wonder	awoke	
war	dwarf		wolf		
	beware		wool		
	awake				

no words	lesson	fuss	scale	biscuit	disc
begin with	assembly	cross	scare	escape	
ss	possible	miss	scrape	escalator	
	scissors	mess	scream	discipline	
	tissue	class	scooter	descend	
	necessary		scene		
	permission		science		
	discussion		scissors		
	expression				

ch at the beginning	cheese	ch in the middle	orchestra	ch at the end	rich
	character	middle	ache	end	match
chair	chorus	kitchen	school	search	switch
chimney	chemical	ketchup	architect	branch	watch
church	child	echo		bench	fetch
chronology					

Unit 18: Same letters, different sound 1: ou, au and ow

ou	route	au	audience	ow	snow
shout	touch	sauce	pause	brown	own
mouse	young	author	aunt	tower	shadow
ground	trouble	applause	laugh	allow	bowl
mountain	famous	autograph	sausage	growl	owe
group	curious			coward	
soup					

Unit 19: Same letters, different sound 2: ar, or, ear and our

ar	swarm	or	word	ear	bear	our
arm	quarter	for	world	fear	learn	pour
card	towards	horse	worse	year	earth	your
march	popular	chorus	doctor	beard	pearl	court
parcel	grammar	corner	motor	weary	rehearse	hour
carve	burglar	forget	visitor	wear	heart	sour
bargain	sugar	orchard	mirror	pear	hearth	flour
war	wizard	work				colour
reward	leopard					

Unit 20: Same letters, different sound 3: igh, augh and ough

igh	weigh	augh	daughter	ough	though
night	eight	taught	laugh	enough	through
sight	neighbour	naughty	draught	bough	brought
frighten	height			cough	thorough

Unit 21: Words with common roots

prime	aquarium	transport	bicycle
primary	aquatic	portable	bisect
primitive	aqueduct	export	binoculars

graph	hydrophobia	microscope	astrology
autograph	dehydrate	microphone	astronaut
photograph	hydroelectric	microbe	asterisk

Unit 22: Extending words

art	exhibit	real	create
artist	exhibition	really	creation
artistic	exhibitionist	realistic	creative
artful		realistically	creatively
artfully			

Unit 23: Suffixes: –able and –ible

–able	changeable	–ible	invisible
breakable	noticeable	accessible	comprehensible
enjoyable	likeable	sensible	responsible
valuable	agreeable	collapsible	divisible
forgivable	irritable	terrible	audible
reliable	inevitable	flexible	legible
enviable			

Unit 24: Suffixes: –tion and –sion

–tion	information	–sion	explosion
instruction	transportation	possession	invasion
collection	exploration	impression	comprehension
production	pronunciation	confusion	expansion
exhaustion	explanation	revision	permission
suggestion	definition	decision	expulsion
operation	competition		
investigation	solution		
population			

Unit 25: Compound words

sets of words	bedroom	other words	scarecrow
fireman	classroom	paintbrush	skateboard
fireplace	cloakroom	goalkeeper	lipstick
fireworks	bathroom	breakfast	penknife
fireproof		cupboard	girlfriend
	snowball	daydream	newspaper
toothache	football	popcorn	doorbell
toothbrush	eyeball	paperback	
toothpaste	basketball		